RAISED BY SQUIRRELS

Los Alamos

story + art: Bram + Monica

RAISED BY SQUIRRELS: Los Alamos
©2006-2007 by Bram Meehan and Monica Banko Meehan

ISBN-13: 978-0-9791093-1-7 · ISBN-10: 0-9791093-1-0

Published by Panel Press
137 Solana Drive · Santa Fe, NM 87501
www.panelpress.com

Second printing November 2007
Printed in USA by Fidlar Doubleday

Raised By Squirrels · email@raisedbysquirrels.com · www.raisedbysquirrels.com

8

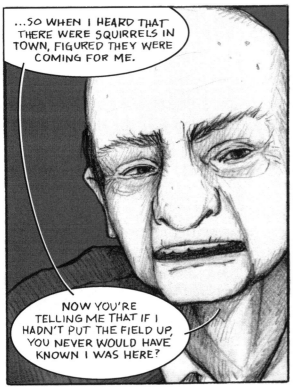

...SO WHEN I HEARD THAT THERE WERE SQUIRRELS IN TOWN, FIGURED THEY WERE COMING FOR ME.

NOW YOU'RE TELLING ME THAT IF I HADN'T PUT THE FIELD UP, YOU NEVER WOULD HAVE KNOWN I WAS HERE?

Los Alamos, Part 2

YEAH, PRETTY MUCH.

BUT WE ARE HERE. WE'VE GOT SOME PROBLEMS AND SURE COULD USE YOUR INSIGHT.

MANHATTAN WAS ON THE HILL.

NANTUCKET — WEATHER CONTROL — WAS UP ON PAJARITO MOUNTAIN.

AND THE ROANOKE PROJECT WAS SET UP UNDERGROUND...

...TO FIGURE OUT HOW TO MAKE SUPERMEN.

OH, THE THINGS THEY DID THERE...

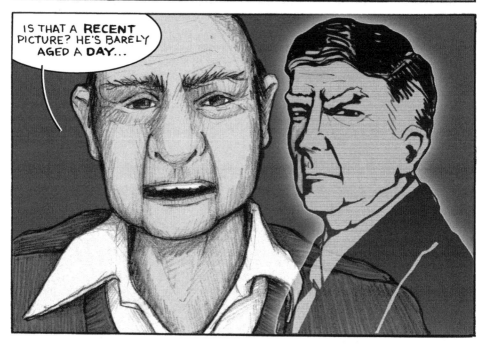

Los Alamos, Part 3
UNDER LOS ALAMOS
ALL THE GOOD STUFF'S LONG GONE
LET'S GET A TEAM IN HERE TO COMB IT.

AND WHAT WAS
DONE TO ME—IT ALL
STARTED HERE.

FINE.

WE NEED TO GO.

Los Alamos, Conclusion

BLAM!

Squirrel Tales

Featuring:

Jeff Kilburn
Dale Deforest
Pete Ziomek
Jeff Benham

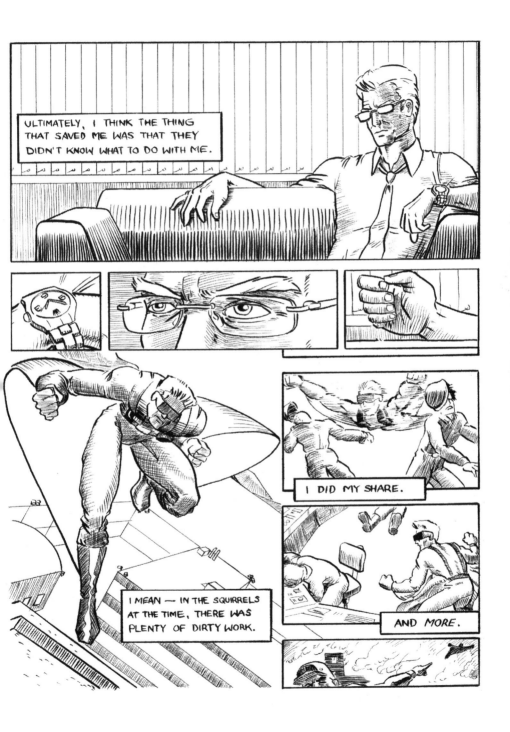

I WAS GOOD, IF THAT'S SOMETHING TO BRAG ABOUT.

BUT — I COULD *FLY*.

PRETTY *UNIMPRESSIVE* COMPARED TO THE REST OF MY SQUAD.

SO THEY WERE *ALWAYS* IN DEMAND. ALWAYS *WORKING*.

AND THAT TOOK ITS TOLL.

STORY + ART: BRAM + JEFF KILBURN © 2006

WITH MY PARTNER.

IN MY PLACE, MOST PEOPLE WOULD'VE CONCLUDED THAT THIS LINE OF WORK'S JUST TOO DANGEROUS...

I DECIDED IT WASN'T DANGEROUS ENOUGH.

STORY + ART: BRAM + DALE DEFOREST · ©2006

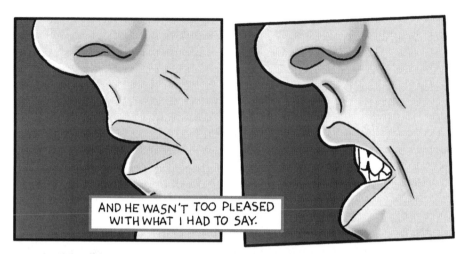

AND HE WASN'T TOO PLEASED WITH WHAT I HAD TO SAY.

THIS ORGANIZATION IS A **VITAL** MILITARY ASSET. YOU **CAN'T** JUST **MOVE OUT.**

EVER SINCE THE SORCERER'S TRIAD WAS FORCED OUT—

—THE PENTAGON HAS ENJOYED A CLOSE WORKING RELATIONSHIP WITH THE S.Q.R.L.

WE THINK MAYBE TOO CLOSE.

AND WITH DIR—FORMER DIRECTOR GABRIEL'S ...**ABRUPT**... DEPARTURE—

—DIRECTOR BOOKMAN THINKS BOTH ORGANIZATIONS MIGHT BENEFIT FROM SOME **DISTANCE.**

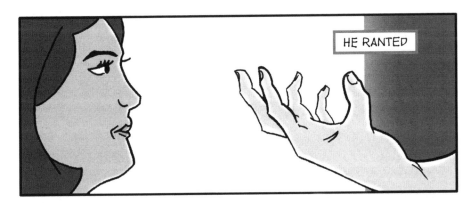

HE RANTED

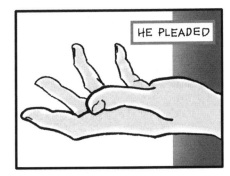

HE PLEADED

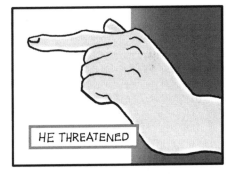

HE THREATENED

BUT IN THE END...

SIR, THIS MEETING IS JUST A FORMALITY.

AS A PART OF D.O.E., DEFENSE HAS NO JURISDICTION OVER US.

STORY + ART: BRAM + PETE ZIOMEK ©2006

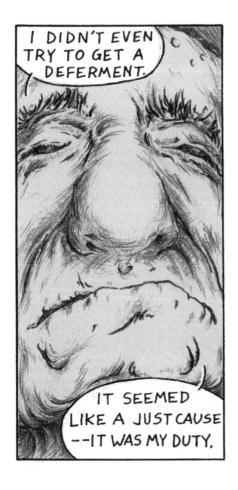

I DIDN'T EVEN TRY TO GET A DEFERMENT.

IT SEEMED LIKE A JUST CAUSE --IT WAS MY DUTY.

AND SO MY NUMBER CAME UP.

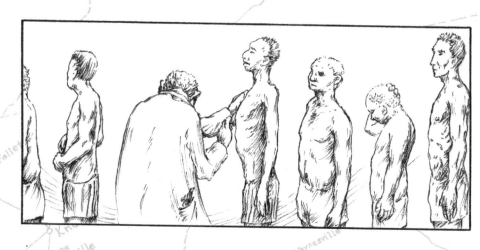

AT THE EXAM, I GOT A VISIT FROM SOME ARMY MEN.

I HAD SOMETHING SPECIAL, THEY SAID, SOMETHING THAT AMERICA NEEDS.

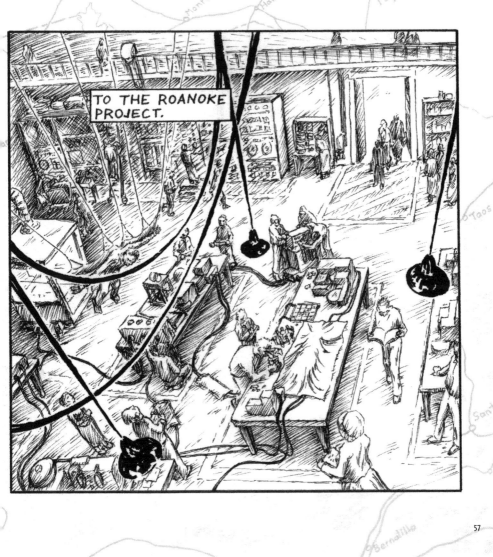

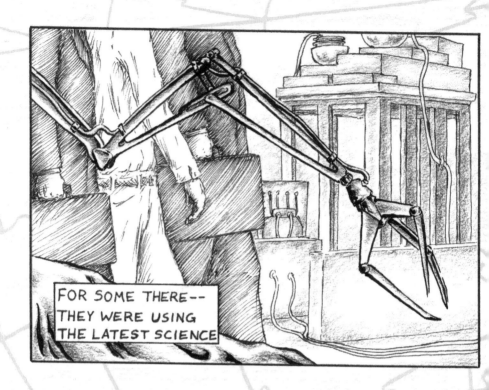

FOR SOME THERE--
THEY WERE USING
THE LATEST SCIENCE

TO GIVE THEM
POWERS.

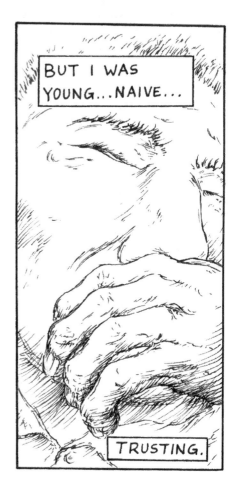

STORY + ART: BRAM + JEFF BENHAM · ©2007

Raised By Squirrels   Gallery

Featuring:

Jamie Chase
Dale Deforest
Matt Dembicki
Marc Haines
JettBOY
Evan Keeling

Marc Haines
xanga.com/deadlyworld

Evan Keeling
dcconspiracy.com

Dale Deforest

7000bc.org

Chase 8/06

Jamie Chase
jamiechasearts.com

CHASE 8/06

Jamie Chase
jamiechasearts.com

JettBOY
myspace.com/theonlyjettboythatcounts

A Young Reginald

Matt Dembicki
waspcomics.com